Welcome to the
SPIDER-MAN
ANNUAL 2009

HI, SPIDER-FANS!

As my most trusted and loyal fans, I've given you access to my personal database! Inside you're gonna discover all about my life, how I got my powers, the secrets of some of my deadliest villains, as well as thrill to two of my teenage adventures!

Hey, gang! I've hidden 6 of my spider-tracers somewhere within these pages. See if you can find them all and then check on page 61 to see if you're correct!

£6.99

THE ORIGIN OF
SPIDER-MAN

THE BEGINNING...

Peter Parker's parents died when he was very young and he was raised by his kindly Uncle Ben and Aunt May in a small house in Forest Hills, New York. Peter's aunt and uncle loved him like he was their own son and tried to instil in him their own good values, including the belief that **"with great power comes great responsibility."**

Peter was very shy and spent most of his time buried in his books studying his favourite subject – science. Consequently, during his years at high school he found himself easy prey for bullies, especially school football star Flash Thompson.

THE WEB OF FATE...

Peter's life was forever changed one fateful day when, during a science trip, he was bitten by a spider that had been bombarded with radioactive rays.

Somehow the spider's DNA fused with Peter's, granting him fantastic powers! Suddenly, the young teenager discovered that he had become incredibly strong and had amazing agility – but that was just the beginning.

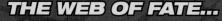

M 1/2000 F5.6

WITH GREAT POWER...

Peter decided that he wanted to be rich and famous, and the best and quickest way was in showbiz. However, first he wanted to try his new powers out and so he fought the wrestler Crusher Hogan in an all-comers competition. Easily defeating Hogan, Peter, now calling himself Spider-Man, embarked on a career in television. Yet fate had one more hand to play.

MONITOR

200

STOP HIM!

WHY? WHAT'S IN IT FOR ME?

COMES GREAT RESPONSIBILITY...

Back stage at the television studio, after Peter's début, a burglar ran past him. Peter could have easily stopped him but he chose not to, thinking that it wasn't his problem.

Later that night however, Peter discovered that his Uncle Ben had been murdered by the same burglar he'd let escape!

Peter was devastated, blaming himself for failing to use his powers when they were really needed. It was at that moment that Peter realised the truth behind his uncle's words and he decided to become a true Super Hero...

and Spider-Man was born!

BITTEN BY AN IRRADIATED SPIDER, WHICH GRANTED HIM INCREDIBLE ABILITIES, **PETER PARKER** LEARNED THE ALL-IMPORTANT LESSON, THAT WITH GREAT POWER THERE MUST ALSO COME GREAT RESPONSIBILITY. AND SO HE BECAME THE AMAZING **SPIDER-MAN**

Looks like Spidey has a full-fledged *reptilian rampage* on his hands! How did the lecherous *Lizard* raise an army of like-minded Lacertilia?

REPTILE!

ZEB WELLS
WRITER

PATRICK SCHERBERGER
PENCILS

NORMAN LEE
INKS

GURU eFX
COLORS

AMANDA CONNER and STRAIN
COVER

DAVE SHARPE
LETTERER

BRAD JOHANSEN
PRODUCTION

NATHAN COSBY
ASST. EDITOR

MACKENZIE CADENHEAD with **MARK PANICCIA**
EDITORS

JOE QUESADA
CHIEF

DAN BUCKLEY
PUBLISHER

Empire State University. Midtown Manhattan.

The Laboratory of Dr. Curt Connors...

Hnnn... I can feel my alter ego, the Lizard, trying to manifest himself...

Keep your head, Connors...if this formula works, you can rid yourself of that demon forever!

Arrr! Can't think...need another dose of antidote!

It's not permanent, but it will keep me human for now...

NO! This is the *original* lizard formula! The one that turned me into a beast in the first place!

How--

I've got to... get...Spider-Man...only he can help...

How could I be so carelesssssssssss

Midtown High School. The Next Morning...

This is a mandatory fitness test. We're being judged against every school in the district, so look alive!

Can we give Parker a sick day? He's gonna make us look bad!

What's that, Flash? I can't hear you from up here...

What the--?

Wow!

Uh-oh, that was dumb. Using my spider-strength in front of the whole class...why don't I just wear my costume next time.

Guess there's only one thing to do...

Convince everyone I'm as weak as they think I am.

Gyaaaarrh!

Ha! I knew Parker couldn't keep that up!

Okay, that's enough everyone! Don't let Parker hold us back!

New York City. Later...

But right now I can't *afford* to let people know I'm really Spider-Man.

Of course, right now I can't even afford a *bus ticket.* I sure hope J. Jonah Jameson will buy some more pictures of Spidey...

But he likes action shots and, wow, it's been kind of slow lately...

Run! Run for your lives!

But, hey! It sounds like the super hero business might be picking up!

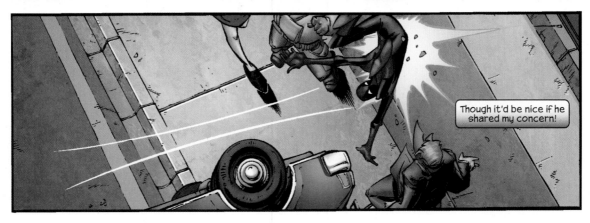

Continued on page 19...

SPIDER-FILE:
SPIDER-MAN

WALL-CRAWLING

The bite of the radioactive spider that gave Spider-Man his powers has granted him the ability to cling to almost any surface. In addition, Spider-Man can use his sticking ability to help grapple his opponents.

SPIDER-STRENGTH

Spider-Man possesses superhuman strength, proportionate to that of a human-sized spider. This allows the wall-crawler to lift approximately 10 tonnes. However, in exceptional circumstances Spider-Man has been known to call upon his incredible willpower and lift as much as 20 tonnes!

SPIDER-SENSE

Spider-Man is gifted with a special sixth-sense, or spider-sense, which alerts him to all forms of danger. This spider-sense has saved the web-slinger's life on occasions too numerous to count. It also aids him while performing feats of amazing agility.

SPIDER-AGILITY & SPEED

Spider-Man is graced with phenomenal agility and speed, which allows him to accomplish incredible acrobatic feats.

WEB-SHOOTERS

After gaining his powers, Peter used his brilliant science skills to create his pair of web-shooters. These remarkable devices fire a thin strand of "web-fluid" approximately 60 ft. The webbing is extremely strong and is designed to dissolve after an hour.

Over the years, Spider-Man has learned to shoot his webbing into many useful forms including concussive web-balls, a parachute and a web-sack for storing his civilian clothing.

Web-Fluid Cartridges

Trigger – Double tap to fire

SPIDER-SIGNAL

Attached to the front of Spider-Man's utility belt is his spider-signal lamp. This torch projects a high-powered spider-symbol that the web-slinger can use to startle his enemies.

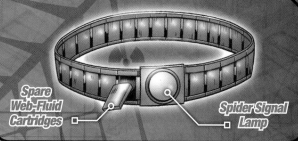

Spare Web-Fluid Cartridges

Spider Signal Lamp

SPIDER-TRACERS

These tiny devices can attach to almost any surface and are special homing beacons with a limited range that trigger Spider-Man's spider-sense. Spidey can throw a spider-tracer and it will attach to the target allowing him to follow his prey wherever they go.

Hey Spidey-fans! This is not one of the Tracers you need to find!

THE BLACK COSTUME

Spider-Man gained his black costume during an adventure on the far side of the galaxy. A god-like being called the Beyonder gathered Earth's mightiest heroes and villains and forced them to fight a war to find out which was stronger – good or evil.

During the conflict Spider-Man's red and blue costume was ruined, so he used a bizarre alien device to create a new costume. The new costume possessed incredible abilities - it generated its own webbing and was also able to change its form to resemble any type of clothing Spider-Man imagined.

Months later back on Earth, Spider-Man's suspicions about his new costume led him to Reed Richards of the Fantastic Four. Reed performed tests that proved the suit was actually an alien creature attempting to make a permanent symbiotic bond with Spider-Man. Reed helped Spider-Man remove the costume and kept it for further analysis. However, it escaped, and, harbouring a deep-seated hatred for Spider-Man, found the perfect host in Eddie Brock, better known as

Venom!

MARVEL FACT

Did you know that when Spider-Man first built his spider-tracers he relied upon a tracking device before he learned to "tune" them into his spider-sense?

SPIDER-FILE: ☢
THE LIZARD

"Big, ugly, exceptionally cunning and with a temper to match, the Lizard is one of my deadliest opponents... The problem is he's also one of my friends!"

Real Name: Doctor Curt Connors
Occupation: Biogenetic Scientist
Base of Operations: New York, USA
Goals: As Connors – To free himself from the curse of the Lizard. As the Lizard – Domination of the world by reptile-kind!

THE LIZARD IS BORN!

Doctor Curt Connors lost his arm while serving as an army surgeon. In the hope of one day restoring his lost limb, he dedicated his life to researching the regenerative abilities of lizards. He developed a formula and tested it on himself. However, it changed Connors into a giant humanoid reptile, consumed with the desire to destroy humankind. Fortunately, Spider-Man was able to use Connor's lab notes to create an antidote and change the scientist back to normal.

Powers and Abilities:

The Lizard possesses great strength, allowing him to lift approximately 12 tonnes. His scaly hide protects him from most injuries, including bullets. Also, his hands and feet are equipped with dangerous claws and, like a gecko, they are covered with scores of tiny spines that allow him to climb any surface.

The Lizard is also equipped with a powerful tale that can whip at speeds of up to 70 mph. In addition, the Lizard has a limited form of telepathy that allows him to control all reptiles within a one-mile radius.

DANGER RATING: 7

THE LEGACY OF THE LIZARD!

Although Spider-Man was able to help his friend, it wasn't over. In moments of extreme stress or exposure to certain chemicals, Connors can still transform back into the Lizard. And whenever this happens, it falls to the wall-crawler to stop him.

MARVEL® FACT

Did you know that the Lizard first appeared in Amazing Spider-Man Vol.1 #6 in 1963!

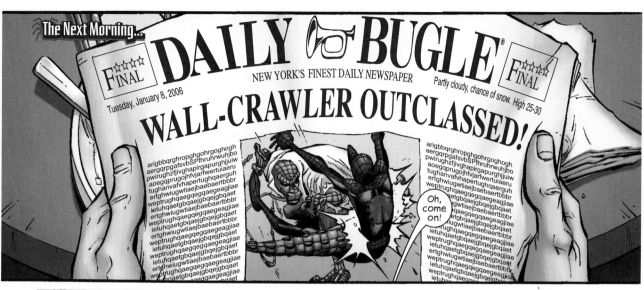

The Next Morning...

DAILY BUGLE

NEW YORK'S FINEST DAILY NEWSPAPER

FINAL · FINAL

Tuesday, January 8, 2006

Partly cloudy, chance of snow. High 25-30

WALL-CRAWLER OUTCLASSED!

Oh, come on!

Something upsetting in the paper?

I made a fool out of myself, Aunt May!

It says that in the paper?

Oh, I mean--no. I was just remembering how dumb I looked in gym class yesterday...

Oh, Peter, you shouldn't get down on yourself just because you're not *athletic!*

Not everyone's a Michael Jordache.

Who?

The point is everyone's good at *something!* You just have to find a situation where you can use *your* gifts! Compete on *your* field!

Hmmmm.

Aunt May means well, but how can I tell her that my real problem is a giant gecko in a lab coat who'll *never* care how special her nephew is...

Yo! Parker!

On second thought, maybe the Lizard isn't so bad...

I had a lot of fun showing you up in gym class yesterday! Wondered if you wanted to show up for basketball try-outs today...

I don't think so, Flash.

See?! There's nothin' I can't beat Parker at!

You heard me!

Nothing?

What was it Aunt May said? I have to compete on my "field"?

How about we both try out for the debate team?

Oh, well... I don't--

Come on, Flash. I thought you said you were better at *everything.*

Well, I...

Fine, Parker! You're on!

Uh, Flash...

Later...

Peter! Peter, wait up!

Peter, that was *amazing.*

Oh, thanks, Liz.

So...what are you doing Saturday night?

Oh, well I--

EEEEEEEEEEEEE!

Getitoff getitoff getitoff!

Liz, try and relax.

They're not attacking... they all seem to be heading somewhere as a group.

B-but where?

Peter?

Sorry to run, Liz...

Continued on page 26...

24...

SPIDEY'S
PUZZLE WEB

"Being a webbed wonder isn't all about fighting! Often you have to out-think your enemies, especially deadly opponents like Doctor Octopus or Venom. So to give you a mental work out I've devised some brain-blastin' puzzles!"

Help Spidey find the names of all these villains in the word grid!

```
N X M U L M I N O
C I K O E U A H I
A B L Q N M K U R
R T L B D E T R E
N O R N O X V W T
A R A Q J G O E S
G S P O A H B G Y
E E L E C T R O M
D R A Z I L U B H
```

SANDMAN
ELECTRO
HOBGOBLIN
CARNAGE
VENOM
MYSTERIO
LIZARD

The Hobgoblin has scrambled the files on some of Spider-Man's most dangerous adversaries.

Can you identify the 4 villains that have been mixed up here?

The Green Goblin is fleeing a crime scene, but Spider-Man is in hot pursuit! Help him catch the crook by choosing a route that avoids the pumpkin bombs and villains!

START ⟩⟩⟩

FINISH

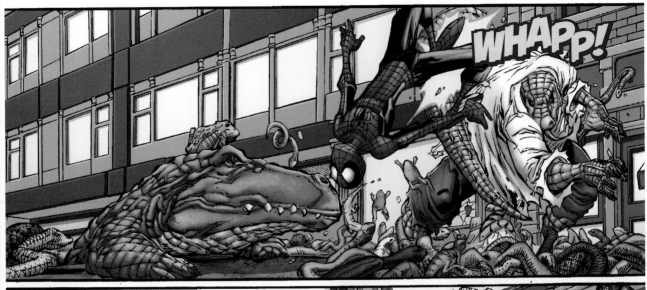

WHAPP!

Yikes!

BAM!

I can't fight back and risk hurting Connors! How am I going to defeat the Lizard without touching him?!

≈Unnnn...≈

Wait a minute...

When Connors is the Lizard he's *cold-blooded!* Maybe I'm just playing on the wrong field!

SAM'S BUTCH

Sorry, *lizard-lips!* Your friendly neighborhood Spider-Man just had an idea!

'S BUTC
BLOCK

Come and get me!

I'm out of here!

CRASH!

Midtown High School. The Next Day...

What's with all the books lately, Flash?

Yeah, let's go!

Beat it!

Studying for the astronomy test, Flash?

What's it to you, Parker?

I don't know...maybe I could help you.

What? You think you're the only smart guy in school?

I bet you didn't even know that *Taurus* was a *bull*.

Flash, that's an *astrology* book.

What?! What's the difference?

Okay, let's start from the top, Copernicus.

Who?

Exactly.

End

31...

SPIDER-FILE:
SPIDER-ART

"Hi, gang! I love to draw! How else do you think I got my snappy red and blue duds? That's right, I designed them myself!

And now you can learn how to draw me too! Just copy this picture, square-by-square, into the empty box underneath it. Then grab your colouring pencils and colour me in!

M 1/2000 F5.6

WEB OF COLOUR

Now grab your colouring pencils and bring this scene of me battling the diabolical Green Goblin to life! Watch out for that pumpkin bomb!

Meanwhile, across town...

Look, Muffy, the Statue of *Liberty!*

Wouldn't it look *smashing* in the lagoon behind the *mansion?* I wonder how much the city would *take* for it--?

Welcome to *New York*, rich people!

BWOMF!

Just like Lady Liberty *says,* "Give me your tired *watches,* your poor *pearls,* your huddled *wallets,* yearning to breathe *free*"...

...that is, unless you want to wind up as *wretched refuse* on my *teeming shore!* Ha ha ha ha ha ha ha!!

I-I've *read* about him--

Th-that's the *Green Goblin!!*

So glad my reputation has achieved *international* stature!

You know, then, that even though I may wear a *smile* on my face, I'm not *joking around!*

Make with the valuables!

Who *says* it's not easy being *green?* HA HA HA HA!!

These days, the very sight of me *coming* makes the rubes fork over cash!

Still, I'm running low on *pumpkin bombs.*

Better pick some up from one of the many *secret lairs* I have sequestered around the city...

Wha-? *no!!*

The hidden entrance to this lair--it's *open!*

My weapons-- *costumes*--vials of Goblin *serum*-- extra *bat glider*-- all *gone!*

It's-it's *impossible!* I-I, the *Green Goblin,* the greatest criminal mind of *this* or any *other* century...

...I've been ⸝choke!⸝ *robbed!*

C'mon, Mr. Jameson, this has got to be the scoop of the week-- the *month*, even!

Spider-Man told me he's switching to his new costume *permanently*...and *you've* got first crack to tell the whole world!

Look at my *door*, Parker! Does the sign on it say *"Free costumed weirdo P.R."*? If it *does*, I want you to call *building maintenance.*

It *should* say *"Publisher"*...

...'cause it's *my* job to prevent photos of some moron in a *body stocking* looking around like he's trying to find his *car keys* from ever *staining* the pages of my *news-paper!*

If you're as chummy with that masked *menace* as you'd like me to *believe*...

...you'd make yourself *useful* and snap some pics of him with his mask *off!* *That* I'd pay *top dollar* for!

Mr. Jameson! We just picked up word on the *police scanner*--the *Green Goblin* is robbing an *armored car* in the middle of the *Brooklyn Bridge!*

Get over *there*, Parker! And if you can't bring back pictures I can actually *print*...forget this address!

Continued on page 45...

SPIDER-FILE: ☢
GREEN GOBLIN

"Incredibly intelligent and totally insane! Plus, he knows my secret identity! That's the reason why the Green Goblin is one of my most dangerous enemies!"

Occupation: Businessman, industrialist and professional criminal

Base of Operations: New York, USA – exact location unknown

Goals: To destroy Spider-Man & rule the New York underworld

BIRTH OF THE GREEN GOBLIN

Norman Osborn was a ruthless businessman and founder of Oscorp. He became the Green Goblin after testing an experimental strength-enhancing formula on himself. Disastrously, the formula had an unforeseen side-effect – it drove Osborn insane. He created the costumed persona of the Green Goblin to hide his respectable identity, and allow him to pursue his evil goals without restraint.

DARK DESTINY

Determined to become the leader of the New York underworld, Osborn decided to make a name for himself by killing Spider-Man. Despite many attempts, the web-slinger always managed to defeat him. His greatest triumph, however, was discovering Spider-Man's secret identity.

Despite many setbacks, the Goblin has dedicated his life to destroying Spider-Man.

DANGER RATING: (8)

Powers and Abilities:

Thanks to the Goblin Formula, the Green Goblin possesses superhuman strength allowing him to lift an estimated 9 tonnes. In addition, the Goblin Formula has granted the Goblin enhanced reflexes, endurance and a healing ability. This power of regeneration, though not as quick as Wolverine's, does enable the Goblin to recover from horrific injuries.

The chemical concoction that gave the Goblin his enhanced abilities also increased his intelligence to gifted levels - but at the price of his sanity.

In an ultimate act of revenge, the Green Goblin used the knowledge of Spider-Man's secret identity to kill Peter Parker's girlfriend, Gwen Stacy, by throwing her off the Brooklyn Bridge!

MARVEL® FACT

Before the Green Goblin had his Bat-Glider he rode a rocket-powered broomstick!

WELL, WELL! SPIDER-MAN PROVED EASIER TO DEFEAT THAN I WOULD HAVE GUESSED! HE FELL IN THAT SMALL SPRING, AND HASN'T COME UP YET! WHAT A TRIUMPH FOR THE GREEN GOBLIN!

HOBGOBLIN

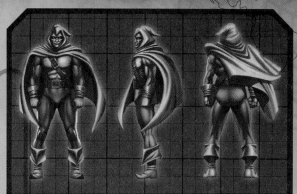

Powers and Abilities:

Through the use of the refined Goblin Formula, the Hobgoblin acquired similar superhuman strength allowing him to lift an estimated 9 tonnes. In addition, the Goblin Formula has granted the Hobgoblin the same enhanced reflexes, endurance and limited regenerative ability.

Interestingly, the improved version of the Goblin Formula that the Hobgoblin developed has inflicted far less damage to the villain's sanity.

The Hobgoblin uses the same basic weapons and equipment as the Green Goblin, but he has enhanced their power.

The Hobgoblin once used an improved version of the Green Goblin's gas weapon. This device not only had a powerful sedative to weaken Spider-Man, but also temporarily deadened the web-slinger's spider-sense!

MARVEL FACT

Spider-Man's classmate, Flash Thompson, was once drugged by the Hobgoblin and dressed in a spare costume in order to fool the web-slinger.

"Corrupt, inteligent, an excellent tactician and utterly ruthless! And that's just Hobgoblin's good points! This is why I hate going up against this guy!"

Real Name: Roderick Kingsley

Occupation: Professional Criminal. Former fashion designer and businessman

Base of Operations: New York, USA – exact location unknown

Goals: Control the New York underworld

THE LEGACY OF THE GREEN GOBLIN

Kingsley was originally a successful but ruthless businessman. However, he harboured ambitions to be something far greater. Opportunity arose when he came into possession of a hidden cache of the Green Goblin's weapons and costumes.

A NEW EVIL IS SPAWNED

Creating the costumed identity of the Hobgoblin, Kingsley attempted to gain control of the New York underworld. His activities, however, quickly brought him into conflict with Spider-Man. Lacking the Green Goblin's original strength-enhancing formula, the Hobgoblin was overpowered and barely escaped capture.

After tracking down Norman Osborn's secret diaries, Hobgoblin was able to acquire the Goblin Formula and refine the chemical mixture to remove the side effects that cursed the Green Goblin with insanity. Despite being almost Spider-Man's equal in terms of strength, the wall-crawler was still able to overcome the Hobgoblin in their next battle.

Determined not to be beaten again, the Hobgoblin now manipulates matters from behind the scenes. However, when the situation calls for it he is not afraid to confront his enemies.

DANGER RATING: 7

SPIDER-FILE: ☢
GOBLIN ARSENAL

The Green Goblin and Hobgoblin share a deadly array of weapons and equipment.

Glove-Blaster

- Sparkle Discharge Nozzle (mixture of iron filings and flash powder)
- Air-Gap Transformer and Firing Electronics
- Knuckle Armour
- Power Supply
- Screw Jack Pump
- Firing Button
- Sparkle Supply
- Safety Button
- Spakle Igniter and Stun Electrodes

Pumpkin Bomb

- Internal Light
- Stem Multi-Position Firing Switch and Timer
- Battery
- Detonator and Stem Electronics
- Explosive Charge
- Manufacturing and Maintenace Access Plate

Goblin Grenade

- Explosive Charge plus optional add-ons like Smoke Screen and Knock-Out Gas Cannisters
- Mylar Covering
- Nylon Support Rods
- Proximity Fuse Detonator

Goblin Bat Glider

Max. Airspeed: 110 mph
Max. Rate of Climb: 90 feet per second
Flight Ceiling: 8,500 feet
Weight – including fuel: 95 Lbs
Overall Length: 43"
Overall Wingspan: 40"
Max. Cargo: 470 Lbs

- Fuel Pump
- Single Axis Gyroscopic Stabilser
- Electric Starting Motor
- Laser Gyroscope Inertail Navigation and Guidance Computer
- Smoke Generator Ring and Canister
- Ultra High Speed/ High Efficiency Micro Turbine
- Batteries
- Actuators
- Goblin Mask Radio Link and Speech Interpretation Logic Centre for hands-free flying
- Main Exhaust and Vortex Shaper
- Vertical Thrust nozzle
- Starboard Steering ram Nozzle
- Turbine Air Inlet and Filter
- Starboard Exhaust Routing
- Flexible-Walled Fuel Tank
- Internal Wing Strengthening Spars
- Electro-Magnertic Foot Clamp and Brace

Graham Bleathman-08

"--if you had bothered to **lock the door behind you** the last time you left!"

"To think I hit on the best boost of my career totally by *accident!*"

"With *your* gear, Greenie, there's no *limit* to the loot I can take!"

Haven't you ever heard of *"finders, keepers"*?

You don't *like* it...

BWOOMF!

BZZRP!

...maybe you should call a *cop!*

HA! HA! HA! HA!

Gone! Blast!

At least I don't have to go away empty-handed!

I hear you're wanted for a *cruise ship* robbery, Gobby!

I won't waste my time with the likes of *you!*

You can't be the *real* Spider-Man-- the costume is *all wrong!*

The wall-crawler would *never* let himself be bested by that...that *copycat!*

Don't quit your day job, wannabe!

Phooey! He flew right over the *water* faster than I could catch up to him--in the middle of the river there's nothing for me to *web-swing* from!

Oh, well...at least I got the *pictures* I needed.

This town isn't *big* enough for me and that sticky-fingered amateur, the Hobgoblin!

I need you to print a *challenge* from *me* to *him*: trial by combat at *midnight* at the place only both of us know--

--for exclusive rights to the *Goblin* identity *forever!*

Look at my door! Does the sign there read "*Free costumed weirdo P.R.*"?

They're blocking the only way out of the room--how can I change into *Spidey?*

What does the *Daily Bugle* get out of this?

Its publisher doesn't get a *pumpkin bomb* shoved up his *left nostril*, that's what!

No deal! Unless you tell me and *only* me where this confrontation is taking place so the *Bugle* has *exclusive rights* to cover it, you can fly right back out that *hole* in my wall!

Oh... very *well*...

And they call *me* crazy...

A-ha! Tomorrow night you'll stake out this address with your *camera!* I have *no doubt* Spider-Man will show up to help out his *best buddy*, the Goblin!

I'm *on* it, J.J.!

We'll catch the web-head *red-handed* this time...I can *feel* it! And for that reason...

...I'm going *with* you!

‡ulp!‡

Hmmm...looks like that *water tower* is where the battle royale will take place...

...we're just *lucky* this apartment across the street became *vacant!*

The *Benjamin* you flashed under the owner's nose probably *helped* in that regard, Mr. Jameson!

That *reminds* me: did you get a *receipt* from that guy?

Ahhhh! My *lucky helmet!* I won my first *Pulitzer* wearing this hat, covering the *war!*

The *war*, huh? That must have been *rough.*

It *was!* The hotel pool wasn't *heated!*

I smell a *bushel* of awards for this story--just as soon as the *wall-crawler* shows up!

Fat chance of *that* happening as long as *flat-top* is watching my every move like a *hawk!*

You know--on second thought, I think I may have accidentally put 1% milk in your espresso, not the *2%* you *asked* for--

I'll be *right back* with--

Never mind *that!* Somebody's *coming!*

Continued on page 54...

SPIDER-FILE: ☢
MOST WANTED

"These are some of my deadliest foes! They all wield awesome powers and they're not afraid to use them to achieve their goals. If you ever see them... Run!"

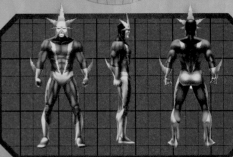

ELECTRO

Real Name: *Maxwell "Max" Dillon*

Occupation: *Professional criminal, former electrical engineer*

BACKGROUND

While repairing a downed power line, engineer Max Dillon was struck by lightning as an unexpected thunderstorm rolled in. The accident granted Dillon incredible electrical powers and he decided upon a more lucrative career: crime. Creating a colourful costume, Dillon became Electro. The villain of voltage has fought Spider-Man on numerous occasions, but always the wall-crawler has outsmarted his opponent.

POWERS: *Electro can generate electricity allowing him to cast bolts of lightning up to 100 ft. He can also use his command of current to travel along power cables, and he has limited control over computers and alarm systems.*

DANGER RATING: 7

SANDMAN

Real Name: *William Baker*

Known Aliases: *Flint Marko, Sylvester Mann, Quarryman*

Occupation: *Professional criminal*

BACKGROUND

A habitual criminal, William Baker was serving time in Rykers Island, a maximum-security prison.

However, Baker, alias Flint Marko, escaped into the desert, and found himself on the beach of an atomic testing site. A huge explosion bombarded his body with massive amounts of radiation and transformed it into a sand-like form.

Marko assumed the name Sandman and has since become one of the most feared criminals in New York. He has fought Spider-Man repeatedly but has always been defeated by the web-slinger.

DANGER RATING: 7

POWERS: *The Sandman possesses the ability to convert all or part of his body into a sand-like substance at will. He can form his body into any shape, and make it hard as rock or as soft and free-flowing as sand. In addition, the Sandman possesses superhuman strength and can lift approximately 85 tonnes.*

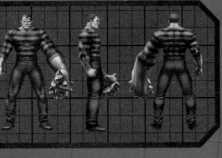

DOCTOR OCTOPUS

Real Name:
Dr Otto Octavius

Occupation:
Criminal mastermind,
former atomic research consultant

BACKGROUND

Otto Octavius was a brilliant atomic researcher who had invented a set of mechanical arms to help in his experiments. In a freak lab accident, he developed the ability to control the arms telepathically. Unfortunately, the accident also caused irreversible brain damage and transformed a respectable scientist into an insane criminal.

POWERS: Each of Doc Ock's mentally controlled mechanical tentacles are able to lift approximately 8 tonnes. In addition, they allow him to travel at great speed and climb up any surface.

DANGER RATING: 8

VENOM

Real Name: Edward "Eddie" Brock

Occupation: Vigilante, former reporter for the Daily Globe

BACKGROUND

Eddie Brock was a reporter whose career was ruined when Spider-Man exposed one of his stories as false. Harbouring an all-consuming hatred for the web-slinger, fortune provided Brock with the perfect instrument for his revenge – the alien symbiote. The two bonded and became Venom – Spider-Man's arch-nemesis. Every time they have fought, Spider-Man has triumphed more through luck than anything else.

POWERS: The alien symbiote grants Brock incredible strength, allowing him to press around 11 tonnes. In addition, the suit mimics Spider-Man's wall-crawling and web-slinging abilities, and does not trigger his spider-sense. Also, the symbiote can protect against small arms fire and can 'stretch' tendrils to grapple opponents.

DANGER RATING: 9

CARNAGE

Real Name: Cletus Kasady

Occupation: Prisoner/patient in Ravencroft Institute

BACKGROUND

Kasady, a convicted murderer, was Brock's cellmate in prison. When Brock escaped, a tiny piece of his symbiote was left behind and bonded with Kasady to form the bloodthirsty monster Carnage. As Carnage, Kasady escaped prison and went on a murderous killing spree. It took the combined efforts of Spider-Man and Venom to defeat him.

POWERS: The alien symbiote grants Kasady phenomenal strength, allowing him to press around 50 tonnes.

Like Spider-Man and Venom, Carnage possesses the ability to wall-crawl and to generate "swing lines" or tendrils, which he uses to web-swing. Like Venom, Carnage can protect against small arms fire and create tendrils to ensnare his prey. In addition, Carnage can create edged weapons like axes or swords.

DANGER RATING: 10

...what's your *name*, masked stranger?

I'm so very, very *tired*.

Parker? Can it *be*?

You're *alive!* What *happened?*

The smoke bomb blew me out of the apartment, but the dumpster by the curb broke my fall!

Fortunately, my *digital camera* was unscathed--I was able to get pics of the *end* of the fight!

Great! Let me *see!*

No, no, *no!* This is *not* what I wanted!

I needed shots of Spider-Man helping the *Green Goblin!*

Why do you think I kept the location of this fight a *secret* in the *first place?*

WHAT?

59...

You mean you *knew* those maniacs were going to fight *here* tonight and you didn't *tell* anybody?!

⸮Heh!⸮ well--you see, in *journalism*, protecting one's *sources* is a, uh, *sacred duty*-- ⸮Heh!⸮

Get him!

Parker! Save me! I'll *double* your benefits!

Mr. Jameson...I'm a *freelancer*... I don't *have* any benefits.

I'll *triple* them then!

We'll have to *run* your photos...tell everyone that *is* Spider-Man in a new costume...

...and say we were working *with* the wall-crawler on a sting to capture the Goblins! It's the only way to stave off the *lawsuits!*

Poor *Jonah*. I don't have the heart to *tell* him...

...that he doesn't *realize* it, but he's actually printing the *truth!*

The End

SPIDEY'S
PUZZLE WEB
ANSWERS

*Now you can find out how well you did!
Remember, Spider-fans, no cheating!*

```
N X M U L M I N O
C I K O E U A H I
A B L Q N M K U R
R T L B D E T R E
N O R N O X V W T
A R A Q J G O E S
G S P O A H B G Y
E E L E C T R O M
D R A Z I L U B H
```

Venom's head

Doc Ock's body

Carnage's arms

Green Goblin's legs

spider-tracers

*Hey, gang!
Did you find all of my hidden
spider-tracers?!! They were on
pages 18, 20, 33, 43, 48 and 59!*

START ⟫

FINISH

WEBS & TENTACLES

"Doc Ock has kidnapped Mary Jane and only you can save her from his evil tentacles!"

Rules

A game for up to 4 players.
Roll a dice and the player who scores highest goes first. Take turns rolling the dice and moving up the board. If you land on a square with a web-line going up from it, move your counter UP the web-line to the square where it ends. If you land on a square with a tentacle going DOWN from it, you must move your counter down the tentacle to the square at the bottom of it. The first player to reach the final square rescues Mary Jane and WINS!

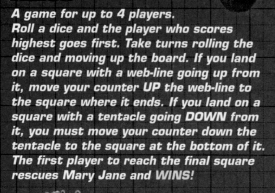

THESE COUNTERS ARE AWESOME TO USE TO PLAY WEBS & TENTACLES! IF YOU DON'T WANT TO CUT THEM OUT THEN PHOTOCOPY THIS PAGE.

START HERE

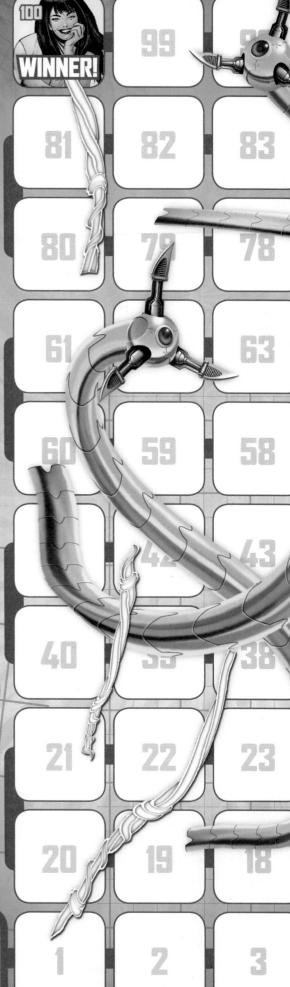

WINNER!   99   98

81   82   83

80   79   78

61   63

60   59   58

42   43

40   39   38

21   22   23

20   19   18

1   2   3